With love, for

....

From ....

Date ....

Memories from your

Mother

AT THE BEGINNING

My Family Tree

Place photo here
Great Grandmother
Place photo here
Great Grandfather
Place photo here
Great Grandmother
Place photo here
Great Grandfather
Place photo here
Grandma
Place photo here
Grandpa
Place photo here
Dad
Place photo here
Me, aged ....

My Great Grandparents

Mom's Maternal Grandparents were

Grandmother .... Heritage ....

Grandfather .... Heritage ....

Their story ....

....

Mom's Paternal Grandparents were

Grandmother .... Heritage ....

Grandfather .... Heritage ....

Their story ....

....

Dad's Maternal Grandparents were

Grandmother .... Heritage ....

Grandfather .... Heritage ....

Their story ....

....

Dad's Paternal Grandparents were

Grandmother .... Heritage ....

Grandfather .... Heritage ....

Their story ....

....

My Grandparents

On Mom's side

Grandpa was called ....

He was born in .... on ....

His family members were ....

....

His job was ....

Grandma was called ....

She was born in .... on ....

Her family members were ....

....

Her job was ....

On Dad's side

Grandpa was called ....

He was born in .... on ....

His family members were ....

....

His job was ....

Grandma was called ....

She was born in .... on ....

Her family members were ....

....

Her job was ....

Early memories
Place photo here

I was born on............................, ... at...

I was named..

My Mom was named ....

My Dad was named ....

My Mom worked as a...

....

My Dad worked as a...

....

My first address was ....

....

....

My earliest memory is ....

....

....

....

Major events that happened the year I was born were...

....

....

....

What I have been told...

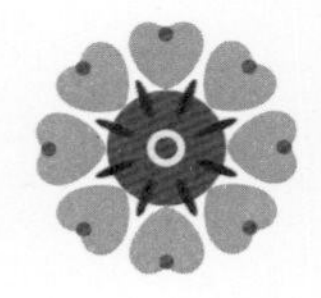

About my birth ....

....

....

How I was as a baby ....

....

....

....

How Mom coped with motherhood ....

....

....

How Dad coped with fatherhood ....

....

....

Place photo
here

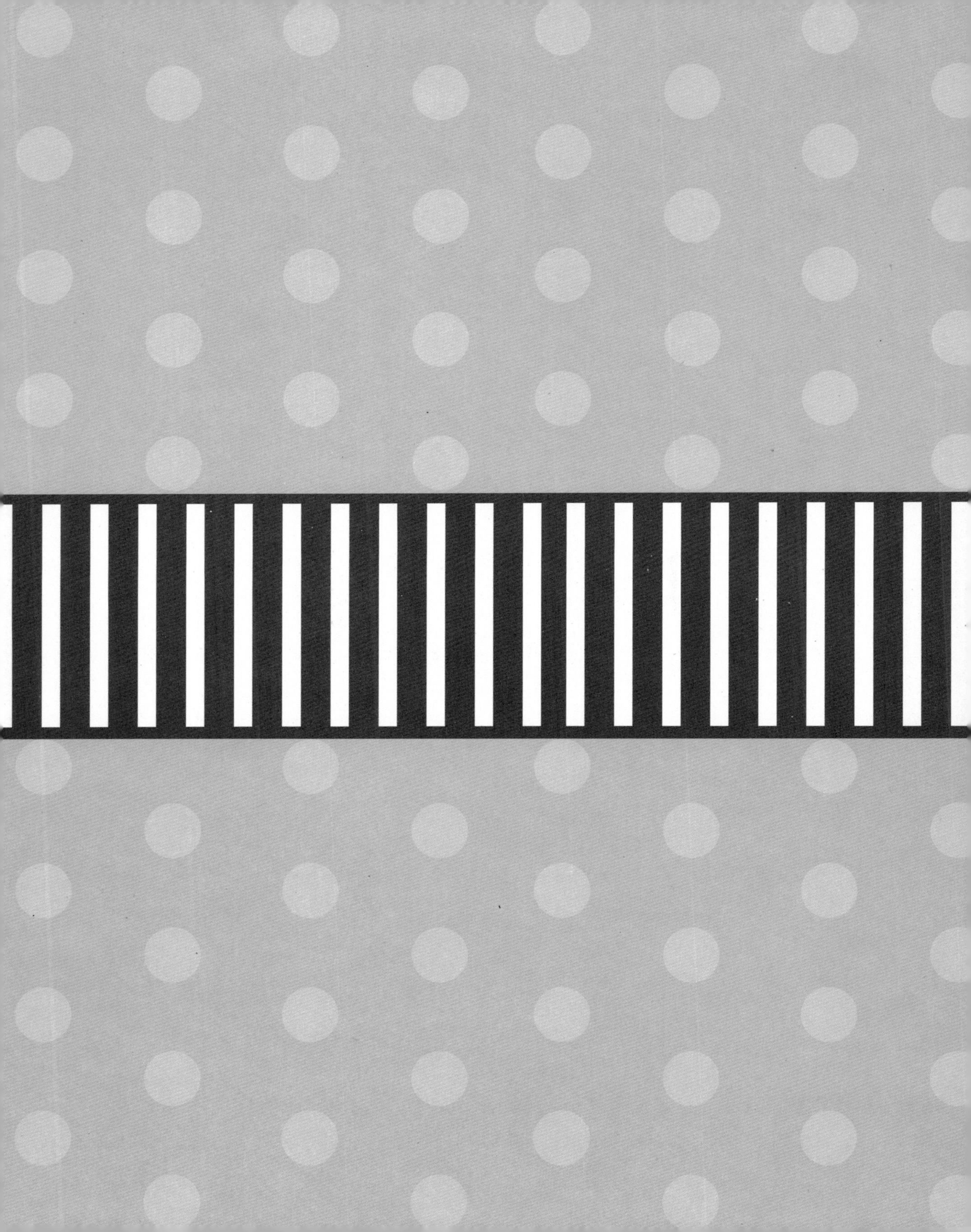

THE FIRST YEARS

My Elementary School Days

My elementary school was named ....

....

My favorite teacher was named ....

....

My friends were named ....

....

....

My favorite subject was ....

....

What I liked about school was ....

....

....

....

....

....

What I didn't like about school was ....

....

....

....

....

What I looked like at school, age ....

The kids on the block

My best friends were ....

We hung out at ....

My friends were great because ....

They would probably describe me as ....

I'm still in contact with ....

Place photo
here

Place photo here
Place photo here

My favorite things...

Song ....

Movie ....

TV show ....

Sports ....

Movie star ....

Singer..

Book ....

Color ....

Food ....

Place to be ....

Place photo
here

Place photo
here

Place photo
here
Place photo
here

I will always remember when...

Place photo here
Place photo here

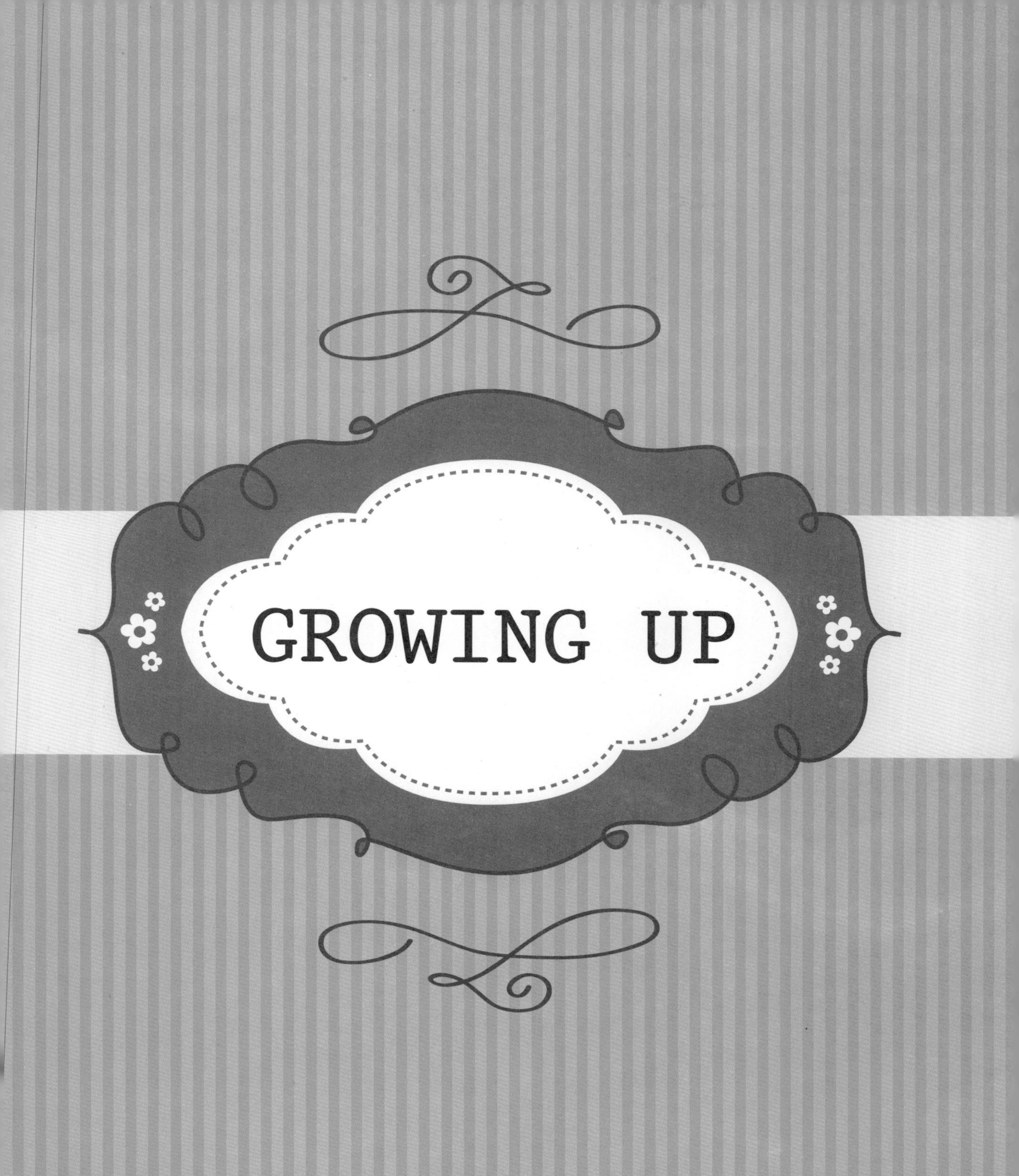
GROWING UP

Vacations with the Family

As a family, we would often go on vacation to ....

....

Other places we went to were ....

....

....

....

....

The best vacation we had when I was young was when ....

....

....

....

....

....

My favorite thing to do on vacation was ....

....

....

....

....

....

....

Place photo
here

Birthday parties

Place photo here

We would celebrate birthdays by ....

....

....

....

We would always eat ....

....

....

....

One birthday is very memorable because ....

....

....

....

The best present I ever received was ....

....

....

....

Place photo
here

My High School...

My high school was named ....

....

I studied there from the year.......................... to..........................

....

My best subject was ....

My worst subject was ....

I was a .... kind of student

My average marks were ....

....

....

When I was at high school, I wanted to be a ....

....

....

The fondest memory of my time there is ....

....

....

School also taught me about ....

....

....

....

....

Place photo here
Place photo here

The Gang...

My group of friends were ....

....

....

....

....

We'd spend our time together ....

....

....

....

I loved them because ....

....

....

Today, I'm in touch with ....

....

....

Where I lived

The address where I lived was ....

....

....

....

I would describe my house as ....

....

....

....

My neighborhood was ....

....

....

....

The best part of the house was ....

....

....

....

....

Place photo
here

Place photo here

Place photo here

Place photo
here

Place photo
here

KEY TO THE DOOR

Me Time

Place photo here
Place photo here

My favorite things

Song ....

....

Movie star ....

....

Singer ....

....

Sports ....

....

TV show ....

....

Outfit ....

....

as a teenager...

Place to be ....

....

....

Person ....

....

Book ....

....

Color ....

....

Band ....

....

....

I will always remember...

Place photo
here

Place photo here

Place photo here

My Sweet Sixteen

My 16th birthday was on ....

To celebrate, we ....

....

....

My guests were ....

....

....

....

....

We ate ....

....

....

I wore ....

....

....

My favorite gifts were ....

....

....

Place photo here

Place photo here

Place photo here
Place photo here

THE NEXT STEP

Graduating High School

I graduated high school on ....

My best grades were ....

....

....

I celebrated by ....

....

For my graduation, we ....

....

....

....

....

....

Place photo
here

My first job

My first job was ....

I got paid ....

....

I spent my first pay check on ....

....

....

....

I thought work was ....

....

....

....

....

....

....

I had this job for ....

....

....

....

Place photo here

Place photo here

Place photo
here

Flying the nest...

I moved out of the family home on...

I was .... years old

The address of my first own place was ....

....

....

....

I lived with ....

....

....

....

I was so excited because ....

....

....

....

My Mom said she felt ....

....

....

....

When I was young, I visited

Traveling

Place photo here

Place photo here

FALLING IN LOVE

Place photo here

Me and Dad

I first met your Dad at ....

The first thing I thought was ....

....

On our first date, we ....

....

....

When he first met my parents, they ....

....

....

When we were dating, we spent our time ....

....

....

The thing I loved the most about him was ....

....

....

....

Wedding bells

Your Dad asked me to marry him on ....

He proposed by ....

....

....

....

We were married on ....

at ....

Our reception was held at ....

....

....

We ate ....

....

....

....

Our first dance was ....

....

....

My favorite part of the day was ....

....

....

....

....

....

Place photo
here

Place photo here

Place photo here

Place photo
here
Place photo
here

Place photo here

Our Honeymoon

We went on our honeymoon to ....

....

....

....

We traveled by ....

....

....

We were away for ....

We stayed at ....

....

....

The best part of the honeymoon was ....

....

....

....

....

....

A home of our own

Our first home together was at ....

....

....

....

We lived there for .... *years*

I worked as a ....

Dad worked as a ....

This was a special time because ....

....

....

....

....

....

Place photo here

Place photo here

Place photo here
Place photo here

Place photo here
Place photo here

THE PATTER OF TINY FEET

We're expecting!

I found out I was first pregnant on ....

When I found out, I felt ....

....

When I told Dad, he ....

....

My pregnancy was ....

....

....

Pregnancy was great because ....

....

....

....

Pregnancy was not so great because ....

....

....

....

Place photo here

Place photo here

Place photo here

My children growing up

I love being a mother because

When you were little you loved to

As a family, we would

Family Vacations

The Holidays

Holidays were always ....

Celebrations would include ....

....

....

....

....

Visitors were..

....

....

We'd always eat ....

....

....

....

The best year was when ....

....

....

....

....

....

Place photo
here

Place photo
here

Place photo
here

Place photo here

Place photo here

THE NEXT STAGE

Place photo here

My children leaving home

My last child left home on ....

At first, I felt ....

....

....

....

....

My daily life changed because ....

....

....

....

....

....

I decided to use this time to ....

....

....

....

....

....

....

Place photo
here

My hobbies

Full circle

The world is different now to when I was young because ....

....

....

....

....

The most important events that have happened in my lifetime are ....

....

....

....

I was at my happiest when ....

....

....

....

My favorite things today are:

Book...

Song...

TV show ....

Movie ....

Place to be..

....

Place photo
here

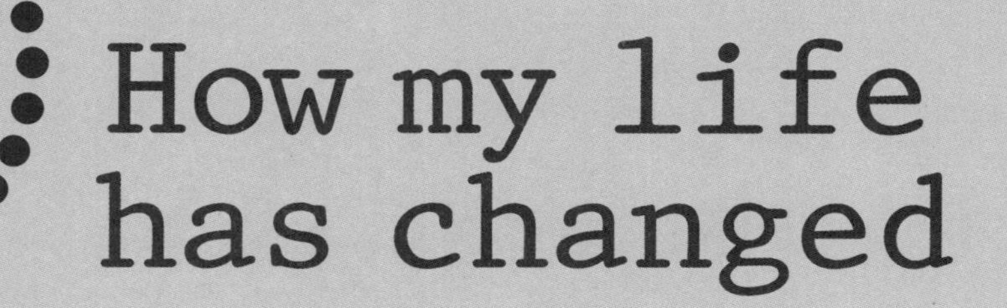

How my life has changed

Place photo
here

Place photo
here

First published by Parragon Books Ltd in 2013
LIFE CANVAS is an imprint of Parragon Books Ltd

LIFE CANVAS and the accompanying logo are trademarks of
Parragon Books Ltd

Designed by Amy Orsborne
Illustrations by Katyakatya

ISBN 978-1-4454-6590-6
GTIN 5060292800974

Printed in China